LOOK AT WHAT'S INSIDE....

THIS AWESOME BLIPPI ANNUAL BELONGS TO:

_____

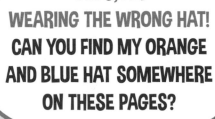

OOPS, I'M WEARING THE WRONG HAT! CAN YOU FIND MY ORANGE AND BLUE HAT SOMEWHERE ON THESE PAGES?

LittleBrother
BOOKS

Published 2021.

Little Brother Books Ltd, Ground Floor,
23 Southernhay East, Exeter, Devon EX1 1QL
books@littlebrotherbooks.co.uk | www.littlebrotherbooks.co.uk

Printed in Poland. ul. Połczyńska 99,01-303 Warszawa

ALL ABOUT Blippi

Wow, look, these pages are all about me! That's so cool!

HEY, IT'S ME, BLIPPI. **BLIPPI!** LET'S SPELL MY NAME TOGETHER! **BLIPPI.**

Trace over the letters to write my name.

Blippi

Blippi begins with the letter B. Circle the things below that also begin with a b.

These are some of the things I love to do. Tick the ones you like doing too.

Play ◯
Dance ◯
Sing ◯
Draw ◯

DO WE LIKE THE SAME THINGS?

My favourite colours are **BLUE** and **ORANGE**.
Can you spot something **BLUE** near you?
Can you find anything **ORANGE**?
Colour the paint splats when you do.

grunt

roar

snap

LET'S EXPLORE

Firefighters climb the ladder to reach tall buildings.

Check out this awesome **fire engine**.

The light flashes when the **fire engine** is in a hurry.

What sound does a fire engine make?

Nee nah ☐

Ring ring ☐

What colour is the fire engine? red

CHEF Blippi

I'm in the kitchen learning all about vegetables. Yum!
Can you spot six differences between these two pictures?

What colour pepper is your favourite?

Colour a number each time you spot a difference.

1 2 3
4 5 6

Circle the vegetable.

SUPER SEASONS

I love how things change throughout the year. Do you? Let's learn more about all the seasons.

IN AMERICA, AUTUMN IS CALLED FALL BECAUSE OF THE FALLING LEAVES.

AUTUMN

In Autumn the leaves on the trees change colour and start to drop to the ground.

Circle the biggest Autumn leaf.

a
b
c
d
e

How many Spring flowers can you count below?

SPRING

Spring is when trees grow their leaves and flowers start to bloom.

Lots of baby animals such as chicks and lambs are born in the spring. Cute!

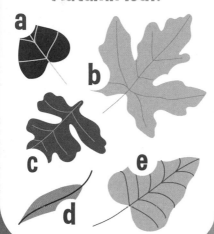

WINTER

Winter is the coldest season. If you're lucky, it might snow!

Trace over the lines to draw the snowflake.

EVERY SNOWFLAKE IS ONE-OF-A-KIND. **WOW!**

SUMMER

It gets dark later in the summer so it's probably still light when you go to bed. That's confusing!

Summer is the warmest season. Beach day, anyone?

Colour this ice cream to keep you cool in the summer sun.

MINT CHOC CHIP IS MY FAVOURITE FLAVOUR. **YUMMY!**

DANCE WITH Blippi

Play your favourite song and copy my dance moves. It'll be so much fun!

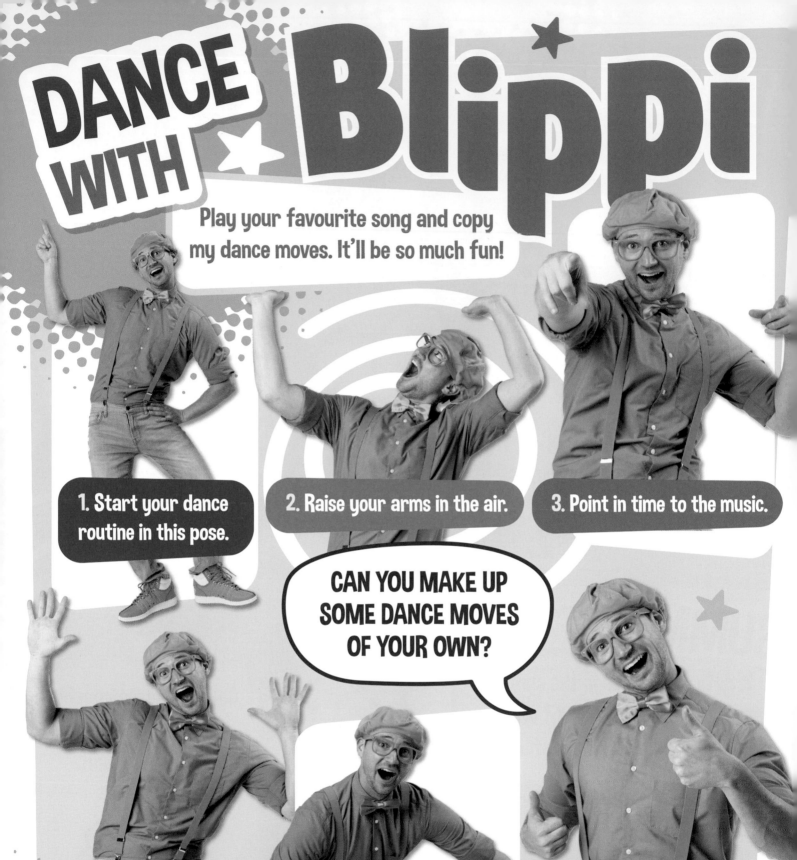

1. Start your dance routine in this pose.

2. Raise your arms in the air.

3. Point in time to the music.

CAN YOU MAKE UP SOME DANCE MOVES OF YOUR OWN?

4. Wave both hands.

5. Crouch down then jump up high.

6. Finish with a big smile and thumbs up!

ALPHABET TIME

Let's take a look at letters and see what we can spell. **I can't wait to get started!**

MY NAME BEGINS WITH THE LETTER B. WHAT LETTER DOES YOUR NAME BEGIN WITH?

THE ALPHABET HAS 26 LETTERS IN IT.

ABCDEFGHIJKLM
NOPQRSTUVWXYZ

Circle the animal that begins with the letter c.

Which letter do all of these things begin with?

Trace over the letters to finish the words.

fish

moon

ball

HANDPRINT ART

ASK AN ADULT TO HELP YOU!

I'm so excited about this hen and chicks picture! It's super easy to make and looks amazing too!

YOU WILL NEED:
- Sheet of A4 paper
- Yellow paint
- A paintbrush
- Red marker pen
- Black marker pen

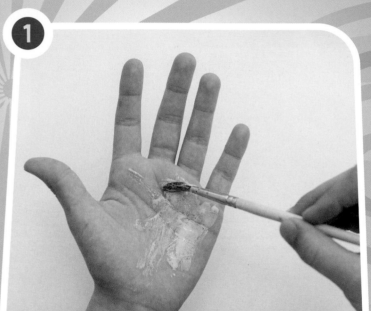

1 Use a paintbrush to paint your hand with yellow paint. MESSY!

2 Press your hand onto the left side of a piece of white paper to make a handprint. COOL!

Blippi BECOMES A DETECTIVE

Read this fun story about how I helped to solve a mystery. **COOL!**

1 One sunny day I went to the park for a picnic. I found the perfect spot and unpacked my lunch. Mmmm, it looked so good!

2 I decided to go for a little walk before I ate. Exercise always makes me super hungry, so I soon headed back for my lunch.

3 When I got back to the picnic table I couldn't believe it...

MY LUNCH AND WATER GLASS HAD GONE!

4 Luckily a Police Officer was passing by so he stopped to investigate. "My lunch has been stolen!" I told him.

5 The Police Officer asked for my help and even gave me a special badge with my name on - how cool is that?

6 We needed extra assistance to solve the mystery of the missing lunch, so a Police dog was called in to sniff out evidence.

7 Soon, the well-trained pooch had sniffed out my water glass. "This is all the evidence we need," the Police Officer told me.

8 We used Police tape to secure the crime scene.

9 Then I took photos of the evidence.

SMILE PLEASE!

10 The Police Officer gave me gloves to put on before I put the glass in an evidence bag. The gloves were one of my favourite colours!

11 Soon the evidence was on the back of a Police motorbike, being taken to the Police Station. Things were getting exciting!

12 At the Police Station, another Police Officer showed me how to dust the glass for hand and fingerprints.

13 Then we used a print lifter, which was like a big sticker, to get print off the glass.

14 The print was so clear. It just needed to be analysed. We were so close to solving the mystery.

15 Soon the results were back. A RACCOON had taken my lunch! I hope they enjoyed it as much as I enjoyed being a detective!

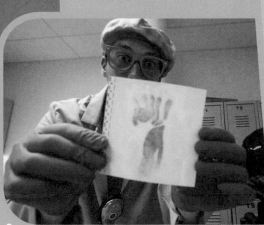

THE END

25

MAKE A MATCH

Look, I'm driving a Police car!
VROOM, VROOM! Can you match the things
I can see on the road into pairs?

DRAW A LINE TO MATCH EACH PAIR.

GREAT JOB!

FUN ON THE FARM

I'm visiting a FARM! Can you help me count the animals?

FINISH

CHICKENS

COWS

START

BLUEBIRD

MAKING FACES

Did you know your face can show how you are feeling? **That's awesome!**

I am smiling because I feel happy

Draw a picture of **HAPPY.**
yourself looking

Now, draw yourself looking **SAD.**

How about
EXCITED.

Practise making different
faces in the mirror to show
different feelings.

Can your grown-up guess
what they are?

Now choose a feeling of your
own to draw.

123
COUNT WITH Blippi

COUNTING is so much fun and super useful. Use the number line to help you solve these counting puzzles.

Count the **RAINDROPS** and fill in the missing numbers.

1 ▪ ▪ 3 ▪ 5

How many **PINK** flowers are there?

How many **YELLOW** flowers are there?

0 1 2 3 4 5 6 7 8 9

How many colours are in the RAINBOW?

5 OR 7

How many CLOUDS are in the sky?

Are their more MOONS or STARS?

MOONS   STARS

THERE'S 1 SUN. THAT'S EASY!

RAINBOW SCIENCE

YOU WILL NEED:
- A white plate
- Sweets with a colourful sugar shell
- A cup of warm water

This colourful candy experiment is so much fun! I CAN'T WAIT TO GET STARTED...

1 Gather together everything you need for the experiment. EXCITING!

ASK AN **ADULT** TO HELP YOU!

2 Arrange the sweets in a colourful circle around the edge of the plate. LOOKING GOOD!

3 Carefully pour warm water into the middle of the sweet circle until the sweets and plate are covered. COOL!

4 NOW IT'S TIME FOR THE FUN BIT! Watch and wait as an awesome rainbow pattern appears in the water.

The sweets are coated in food colouring and sugar. When you pour water on them, the coating dissolves and spreads through the water making it the colour of the sweets. **AMAZING!**

THAT'S SO COOL!

IT'S PLAYTIME!

Trace over the dotted line to see who I'm playing with today.

Can you spot this bird somewhere on this page?

WOW! HE'S A CUTIE!

FRUITY FUN

Do you know your apples from your pears? Use the fruit pictures to help you fill in this crossword.

o r a n g e

p

p e a r

l

c h e r r i e s

SPOTTED!

Wow, I've gone back in time to when dinosaurs lived on Earth! Cool! **Can you spot all of the dinos below in the big picture?**

Tick off each dinosaur as you spot it.

GO DINO!

Get moving with these super fun dinosaur actions.

1 Stomp like a **STEGOSAURUS.**

2 Swing like a **ANKYLOSAURUS.**

3 Stretch up high like a **DIPLODOCUS.**

4 Prowl like a **SPINOSAURUS.**

5 Flap your arms like a **PTERODACTYL.**

6 Roar like a **TYRANNOSAURUS.**

7 Chomp like a **TRICERATOPS.**

I'M A TYRANNOSAURUS! ROAR!

8 Pretend to hatch like a **BABY DINOSAUR.**

PICNIC TIME

Mmmm, look at all this yummy food.
Trace over the lines to finish the picnic.

Tick the boxes when you have drawn these SHAPES.

Circle

Semi Circle

Square

Triangle

What shape is a DOUGHNUT?

Square

Circle

Blippi VISITS AN APPLE FACTORY

Have you ever wondered how an apple gets from a tree to the supermarket? **LET'S FIND OUT TOGETHER.**

1 Apples grow in an orchard. You need a ladder to reach the high up ones. I hope it's not wobbly!

2 Every single apple has to be handpicked and put in a bin - that's a long job!

3 When the bin is full the tractor picks it up and takes it away.

BUH BYE!

4 All of the bins full of apples are loaded onto a truck by forklift.

5 Then the apples are driven to the apple factory.

6 At the factory, a forklift unloads the apple bins.

SEE YOU THERE!

7 The apples are washed in water and scrubbed clean.

8 After a quick rinse, the apples go through giant fans to dry them.

9 Then they get sorted into ones that look tasty and ones that don't. The ones that don't look so good are made into apple pie. Yum!

LOOK, THE APPLES ARE HAVING A BATH!

10 Next, a machine gives each apple a sticker. Then they're put on what I like to call apple beds.

11 The apples beds are put into boxes and a machine closes lids. How cool is that?

12 The boxes are stored in a giant fridge while we wait for the truck to arrive.

13 The truck's here! Now the apples are loaded on. They're almost ready for you to eat!

14 The truck delivers the apples to the supermarket.

15 The apples are unloaded onto the supermarket shelves ready to buy. What an exciting journey they've had!

VROOM VROOM!

THE END

Blippi COLOURS

BLUE

My favourite colour is...

BLUE is the colour of the sea.

The sky is BLUE.

Draw some more blue fish so this one has some friends.

Trace over the waves so that the blue whale is swimming in the sea.

MY SHIRT IS BLUE.

Which of these blue birds is the odd one out?

And my other favourite colour is... **ORANGE**

ORANGE is the colour of crunchy carrots. MUNCH MUNCH!

Colour this orange orange. THAT'S FUNNY!

Traffic cones are often ORANGE. The bright colour makes them easy to spot.

MY GLASSES ARE ORANGE.

Which of my orange bowties it the biggest?

a
b
c
d

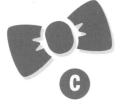

How many ORANGE BALLOONS can you count?

Answers on pages 76-77.

CAMP OUT

Can you finish the jigsaw of me and my FRIENDS camping? Draw lines to match the missing pieces to the picture.

1

a

CAMPING IS SUCH AN ADVENTURE!

What INSTRUMENT am I playing?

Piano

Guitar

Do you like CAMPING? Draw a circle around your answer.

YES   NO

How many FRIENDS are camping with me?

ALL ABOUT ELEPHANTS

Hey, look at these ELEPHANTS! Let's find out more about them.

Elephants are the biggest land animal in the world. **WOW!**

Elephants spend most of the day eating. They like roots, grass, fruit and bark.

THAT'S SO COOL!

What colour are ELEPHANTS?

SPOTTED!

Which close up is of the elephant?

a

b

c

Elephants use their **trunks** like a straw to suck up water. **COOL!**

Elephants love bananas. **How many bananas can you count?**

A baby elephant is called a calf. They can walk within an hour of being born. **AMAZING!**

Answers on pages 76-77.

MARVELLOUS MUSIC

My favourite song is about a small star that twinkles.

Can you guess what the song is called?

You can play it, listen to it, sing to it and dance to it! That's so cool!

What's your favourite song? CAN YOU SING IT?

THERE ARE LOTS OF DIFFERENT KINDS OF MUSICAL INSTRUMENTS. SOME HAVE STRINGS, SOME YOU BLOW AND SOME YOU BANG.

Which of these instruments do you BANG?

Look, I'm dancing to 'Head, shoulders, knees and toes'. Can you put the pictures in the right order?

a

b

c

d

WHAT KIND OF MUSIC ARE BALLOONS AFRAID OF?

POP MUSIC!

Draw lines to match each instrument to its name.

xylophone   guitar   keyboard

ON THE MOVE

Look at these vehicles GO, GO, GO! Follow the trails they've made with your finger or a pencil.

CHOO!

CHOO!

SPLASH!

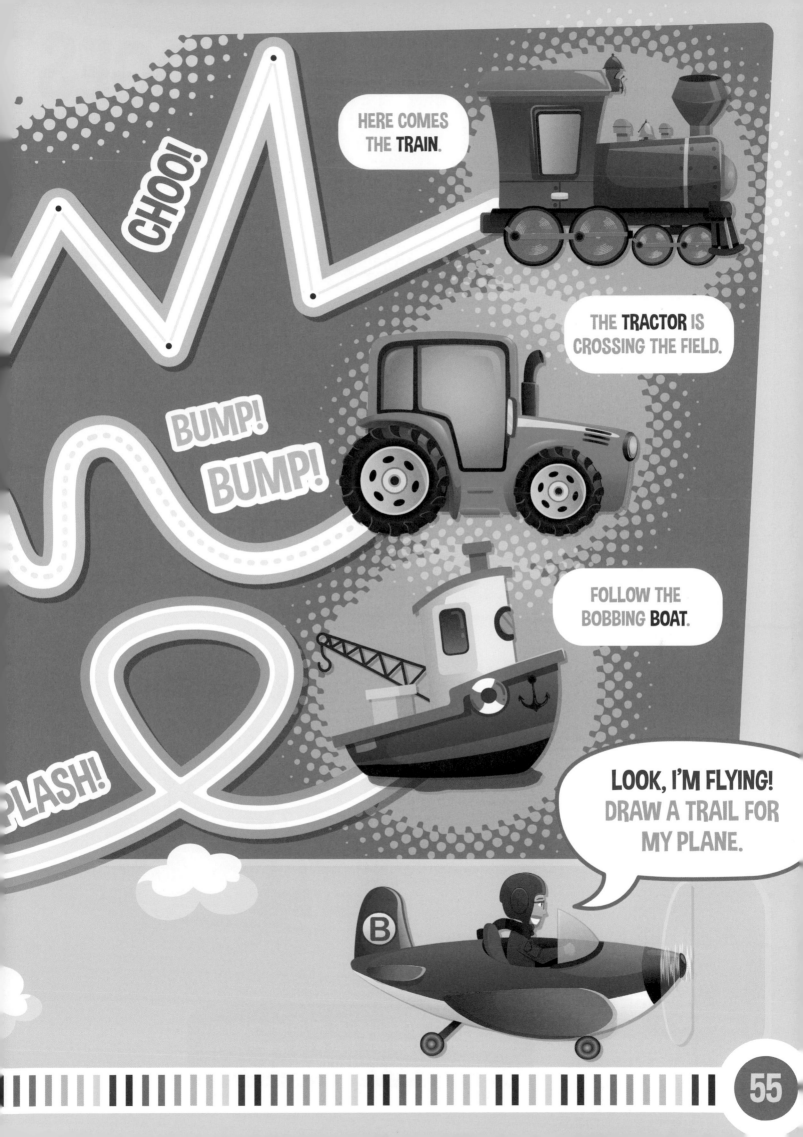

Blippi BADGES

Make and wear these colourful Blippi badges.

YOU'LL LOOK AWESOME!

YOU WILL NEED:
- Thin Card
- Glue
- Scissors
- Safety Pins
- Sticky Tape

ASK AN ADULT TO HELP YOU!

HOW TO MAKE:
1. Cut out these pages and glue them onto thin card. **STICKY!**
2. Carefully cut the badges out along the dotted lines. **GO SLOW!**
3. Attach a safety pin to the back of each badge with sticky tape.
4. PIN YOUR BLIPPI BADGES TO YOUR CLOTHING OR BAG FOR EVERYONE TO SEE!

Blippi

Make sure you've read pages 55 and 58 before you cut out the badges. If you don't want to cut up your Annual, photocopy or scan and print the pages instead.

COUNT with ME!

LEARN & PLAY

WOW LOOK AT THAT!

HellOooOOO!

Wooooooo!

ABC

WOW!! LOOK AT THAT!

THAT'S SO COOL!

UP IN THE SKY

All of these things belong in the sky. Can you match each one to its shadow?

1
2
3
4
5

Which of these vehicles is made for flying in the air?

a

b

c

kite

Trace over the letters to write the name of something else that can fly.

a

b

d

c

e

Colour in your own flying kite using your favourite colours. **WOW!**

DAY AND NIGHT

There are lots of differences between day and night. Which ones do you know?

DAY

In the **DAYTIME** the sun shines making it light.

The sun gives off heat so **DAYTIME** is the warmest part of the day.

DAYTIME is when we play. Trace over the dotted lines to bounce this colourful ball.

We go outside in the daytime. Tick what you put on your feet when you go outdoors.

Flowers open their petals during the day. Can you circle the tallest flower?

a   b   c

NIGHT

Stars appear at night. If it isn't cloudy, you can see them twinkling in the sky.

How many STARS can you count here?

Night is when most people sleep. Do you take a teddy to bed with you? Draw your favourite soft toy here.

Some animals, such as **OWLS** sleep in the day time and are awake at night.

I'M FEELING SO TIRED NOW. Trace over the snores to send me to sleep.

ZZZ ZZZ ZZZ

Answers on pages 76-77.

ACTION MATCH

Hey, what am I doing here? Draw a line to match each picture to the right action.

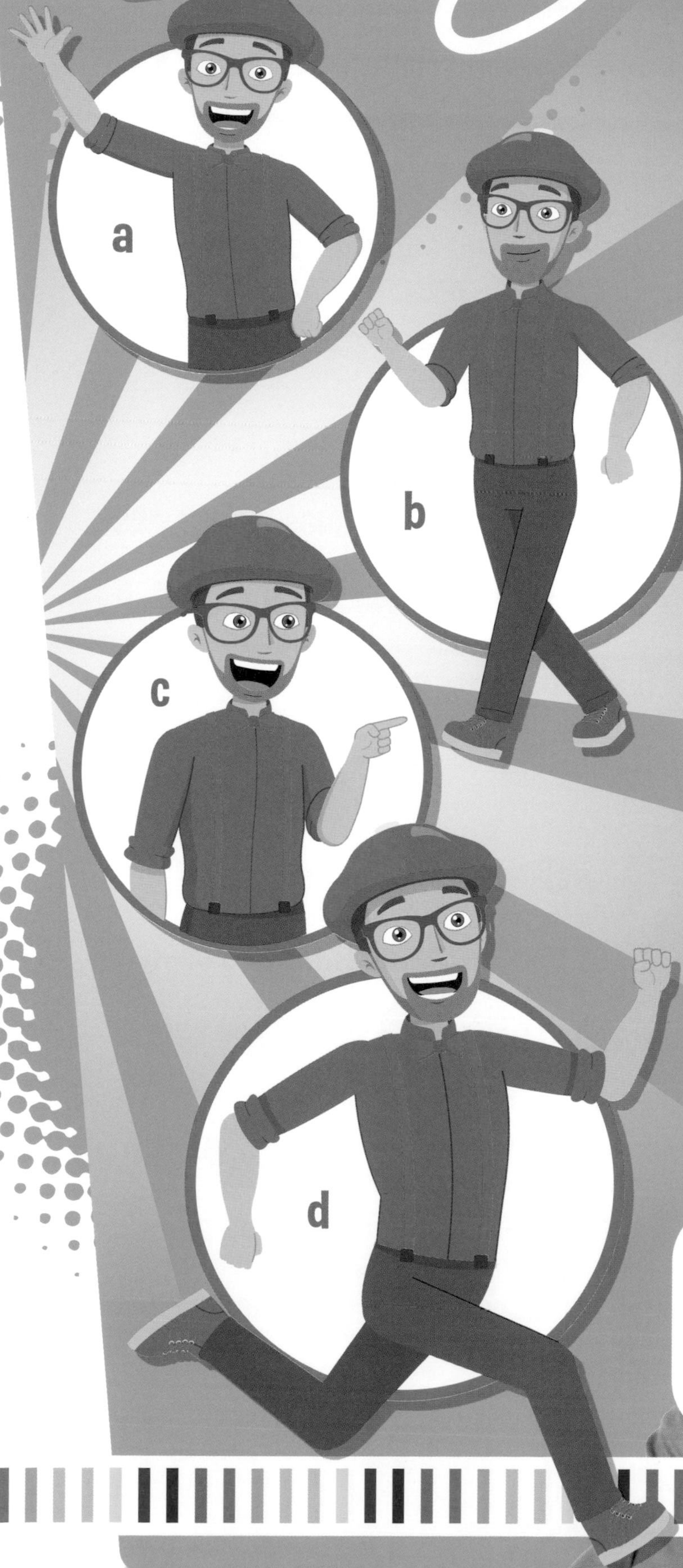

a

b

c

d

WALKING

WAVING

RUNNING

POINTING

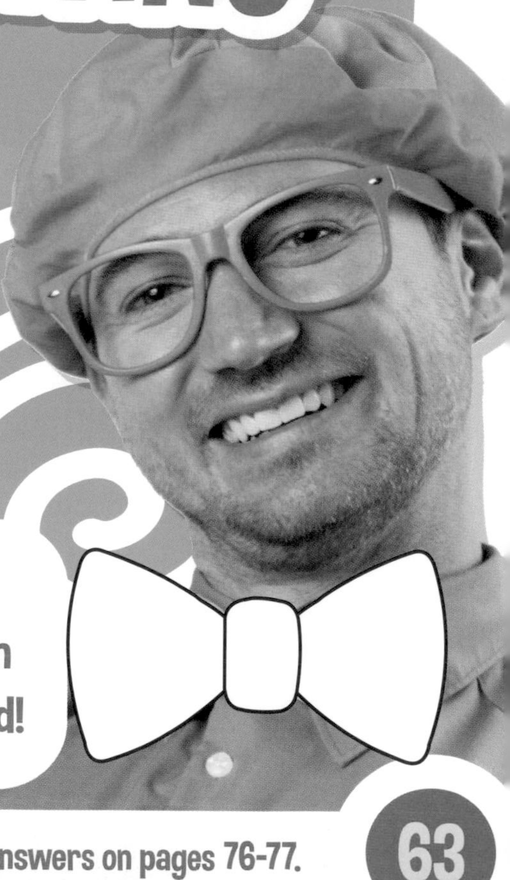

Colour my **BOWTIE** when you've finished!

Blippi AND THE BALLOON

One day, the ☀ was shining and I was feeling super happy because I was on my way to my friend's party. I had a 🎈 to give to him, in his favourite colour.

But just as I reached the end of my friend's street, there was a huge gust of wind. The 🎈 blew out of my hand and floated away! I felt sad that I'd lost my 🎈. "Maybe I can find it before I get to the party," I thought to myself.

Just then, a girl eating an 🍦 walked past with her dad. "Hi, I'm 👨," I told them. "My 🎈 has floated away. Have you seen it?" The girl shook her head. "I hope you find your 🎈 soon," she said.

A little further down the street, there was a boy bouncing a 🏀 with his big sister. "Hi, I'm 👨," " I told them. "My 🎈 has floated away. Have you seen it?" But they hadn't seen my 🎈 either.

SUN
BALLOON
ICE CREAM
BLIPPI
BALL
KITE

When you see a picture, say the word out loud.

I was almost at the party when I spotted a family carrying a .

"Hi, I'm ," I told them. "My has floated away. Have you seen it?"

None of them had. "Good luck finding your ," the mum said.

A moment later, I arrived at my friend's house. "I wish I hadn't lost the ,"

I thought, sadly. Just then, something caught my eye. Can you believe what I

saw? There, with its string tangled up in a bush, was my ! I untangled

the string and held on to it tightly. This wasn't going to escape again!

I knocked at the door and my friend answered. "Hi ," he said,

"thank you for coming". "This is for you," I said, handing him the .

"Thank you . That's my favourite colour," my friend replied.

I had a great time at the party. I was so happy that the had managed

to find its way there too, all by itself. What a clever !

THE END

If you have a healthy diet, it's OK to have a treat sometimes. Circle the sweet treat you would choose. **YUM!**

How many shiny red apples are growing on this apple tree?

Which juicy pear is the odd one out?

a

b

c

Trace over the letters to reveal my favourite vegetable.

Make sure you drink lots of water every day too. **GLUG! GLUG! GLUG!**

Answers on pages 76-77.

SEASIDE FUN

ASK AN ADULT TO HELP YOU!

HELLO, I'm at beach. Cut out the pictures opposite and stick them to the scene.

Make sure you've read page 70 before you cut out the pictures. If you don't want to cut up your Annual, photocopy or scan and print the pages instead.

SPACE ADVENTURE

Let's play astronauts and blast into space!
5-4-3-2-1 LIFT OFF!

Our solar system is made up of eight planets, the sun and the moon. There are also dwarf planets, other moons, comets, asteroids, space rocks and ice. **AWESOME!**

DID YOU KNOW?
The sun is actually a gigantic star. **WOW!**

We live on **PLANET EARTH**. It's the only planet in the solar system known to have life on it.

earth

Astronauts have visited space and have even walked on the moon. **AMAZING!**

MARS is known as the red planet because of its colour.

Can you spot three differences between these two space rockets?

The planet Saturn has rings made of ice and rock. HOW COOL IS THAT? Use your favourite pens to colour this picture of Saturn.

Can you spot this SHOOTING STAR somewhere on these pages?

Answers on pages 76-77.

DETECTIVE Blippi

Can you help me use the clues below to work out which animals are being described? **It's just like being a DETECTIVE!**

I LIVE ON A FARM.

I MAKE MILK.

I SLEEP IN THE DAYTIME.

I CAN FLY.

I HAVE A WOOLLY COAT.

I LIVE IN A FIELD.

I CAN SWIM ON WATER.

I HAVE A BEAK.

Use these pictures to help you solve the puzzle.

OWL   SHEEP   DUCK   COW

I SAY
Moo Moo ★ → I AM...
_ _ _ _ _ _ _ _ _ _ _ _ _

I SAY
Hoot Hoot ★ → I AM...
_ _ _ _ _ _ _ _ _ _ _ _ _

I SAY
Baa Baa ★ → I AM...
_ _ _ _ _ _ _ _ _ _ _ _ _

I SAY
Quack Quack ★ → I AM...
_ _ _ _ _ _ _ _ _ _ _ _ _

Answers on pages 76-77.

COLOUR PATTERNS

Spotting patterns is awesome! Can you work out what colour the picture at the end of each row should be.

COLOUR THE LAST PICTURE THE RIGHT COLOUR.

Answers on pages 76-77

COPY Blippi

THIS IS SO FUN !

Do you like playing games? Then grab a dice and copy me!

How to play

Take it in turns to roll a dice and copy the action for the number it lands on. Keep playing until each player has completed every action, or for as long as you like.

ANSWERS

Pages 6-7 - All About Blippi
Bird, boat, balloon and banana begin with the letter b.

Pages 8-9 - Party Time

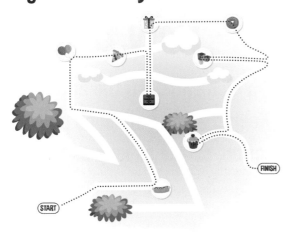

Pages 10-11 - Day out with Blippi
Flower a is the biggest.

Pages 12-13 - Let's Explore
A fire engine's siren makes a nee nah sound.
Close up c isn't from the fire engine.

Pages 14-15 - Chef Blippi
The carrot is the vegetable.

Pages 16-17 - Super Seasons
Leaf b is the biggest.
There are 6 flowers.

Pages 20-21 - Alphabet Time
Cow begins with the letter c.
Strawberry, stars and sun begin with the letter s.

Pages 26-27 - Make a Match

Pages 28-29 - Fun on the Farm
1 bird, 1 bluebird, 3 ducks, 4 chickens,
2 cows, 3 pigs, 4 horses, 4 sheep.

Pages 32-33 - 123, Count with Blippi
2 pink flowers and 4 yellow flowers.
7 colours in the rainbow.
5 clouds in the sky.
More stars than moons.

Pages 38-39 - Spotted!

Pages 42-43 - Picnic Time

The doughnut is a circle shape.

Pages 46-47 - Blippi Colours

Bird d is the odd one out.
Bowtie d is the biggest.
There are 4 orange balloons.

Pages 48-49 - Camp Out

Blippi is playing the guitar.
There are 2 friends.
1 - c, 2 - a, 3 - d, 4 - b.

Pages 50-51 - All About Elephants

Elephants are grey.
Close-up c is of the elephant.
There are 4 bananas.

Pages 52-53 - Marvellous Music

Blippi's favourite song is 'Twinkle, Twinkle
Little Star'.
You bang the drum.
The correct order is a, d, b, c.

Pages 58-59 - Up in the Sky

1 - b, 2 - e, 3 - d, 4 - c, 5 - a.
b. The plane can fly.

Pages 60-61 - Day and Night

You put shoes on to go outside.
b is the tallest flower.
There are 5 stars.

Page 63 - Action Match

a - waving, b - walking, c - pointing,
d - running.

Pages 66-67 - Yummy Food

There are 5 apples on the tree.
Pear b is the odd one out.
Blippi's favourite vegetable is a carrot.

Pages 70-71 - Space Adventure

Pages 72-73 - Detective Blippi

1. cow, 2. owl, 3. sheep, 4. duck.

Page 74 - Colour Patterns

1. green, 2. red, 3. orange.